Terence the Toilet

Travels The World

by Ann Louise Stubbs

Crombie Jardine
PUBLISHING LIMITED

13 Nonsuch Walk, Cheam, Surrey, SM2 7LG
www.crombiejardine.com

First published by
Crombie Jardine Publishing Limited in 2006

ISBN 1-905102-53-4

Written & illustrated by Ann Louise Stubbs

Designed by www.glensaville.com
Printed & bound in Belgium by Proost

for Mum and Dad

Terence was your average
bog-standard toilet.

Most of the time he was a
fairly laid-back kinda guy:
he just went with the flow...

...but lately he was getting
blocked up more and more often
and a couple of times he had
come close to overflowing...

The problem was he was feeling
<u>restless</u> after reading the
magazines in the bathroom...

'Blimey!' he thought, 'all these
exotic bathrooms in exotic places
all over the world and here
I am staring at the same four walls
day in and day out!'

He thought,

I want to find a more _interesting_ place to live and lead a more _exciting_ and _exotic_ life!

So he called a cab,
went straight to the airport...

...and got the first flight
he could get!

He went to the biggest cities in the world, where he met highflying corporate toilets on Wall Street with state-of-the-art anti-gravity power-flush devices...

Targets!
Performance!!
Deadlines!

...and lunched with the sophisticated bidets of Parisian hotels and learnt all about the history of butt rinsing etiquette...

"The first flush appeared during the Renaissance... then came the Impressionists who took the art form to a whole new level... blah blah."

...then he ventured <u>even</u> <u>further</u> afield
to the parched African plains to see
the roaming portaloo tribes
he had heard so much about...

'Our nomadic way
of life means we
never see the same
butt twice.'   'Fascinating!!'

...and right into the heart of the Australian outback where he learnt all about the benefits of composting from local the longdrops...

"We call it a fair-dinkim Down-to-Earth approach eh mate."

19

He travelled to the balmy
Tropics to witness the
beautiful dawn flushing chorus
of the magnificent
Toilets of Paradise...

...and <u>even</u> managed to track down
the famously elusive pygmy toilets
of the Amazon Rainforest...

He travelled far and wide
and saw so many different places
and so many different ways
of life...

...but he still felt <u>restless</u>...

...and he still didn't know
<u>where</u> to live!

So he decided he would make <u>one</u> <u>more</u> <u>trip</u> to find a <u>guru</u> <u>toilet</u> he had heard about that was living in the Himalayan mountains...

For weeks and weeks he trekked across dangerous crevasses and scaled perilous mountain peaks in search of the guru...

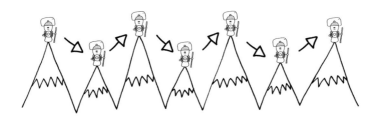

...but no matter how <u>hard</u> he tried...

...he could not find the guru anywhere!

..."This is hopeless," he thought,
"there is no guru toilet here"
and he felt totally <u>defeated</u>...

...so exhausted he could barely
bring himself to flush,
he began to make his
way back down the mountain...

Then suddenly he heard a faint
voice and yes!
there it was again!

Terence looked down but
all he could see was a hole
in the ground...

Suddenly, the hole spoke!
"Wait!" it said
"I am the guru you seek!"

Terence laughed and laughed
until he nearly overflowed, and said,
"But how can you be a guru?
You are just a hole in the ground!"

There was an eerie silence, and then the hole spoke...

"Why, this is <u>wonderful!!</u>"
Terence exclaimed
"<u>at last</u> I have found you!"

"Please, oh wise guru toilet,
I have travelled so far,
I have seen so many places,
but I still do not know
where I belong!

Where should I go next?!!"

There was another
eerie silence and then
the hole spoke again...

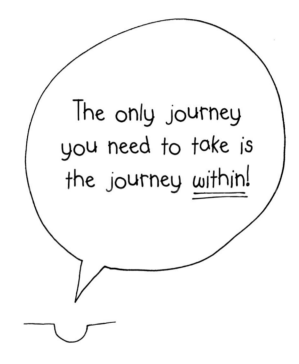

Suddenly there was a loud
explosion!!!

...followed by a great
plume of smoke!!

...and when the smoke cleared,
instead of <u>one</u> hole...

...there were now
two!!

www.crombiejardine.com

www.annlouisestubbs.co.uk

Barry the Butter Blob

discovers

The Meaning of Life

by Ann Louise Stubbs

Also available by Ann Louise Stubbs

1-905102-55-0 · £4.99

Terence the Toilet was your
average conscientious bathroom
fitting until he got the
travel bug and embarked
on the greatest adventure
of his life